The Twelve Days of Christmas Cats

The Twelve Days of
CHRISTMAS CATS

by Don Daily

COURAGE
BOOKS

AN IMPRINT OF RUNNING PRESS
PHILADELPHIA · LONDON

9   8   7   6   5   4   3   2   1
Digit on the right indicates the number of this printing

Library of Congress Cataloging-in-Publication Number 98-70170

ISBN 0-7624-0384-5

Designed by Frances J. Soo Ping Chow

This book may be ordered by mail from the publisher.
Please include $2.50 for postage and handling.
But try your bookstore first!

Published by Courage Books, an imprint of
Running Press Book Publishers
125 South Twenty-second Street
Philadelphia, Pennsylvania 19103-4399

For my daughter Susie, whose love
of cats inspired this book.

On the first

day of Christmas my true love gave to me

A kitten in a fir tree.

On the second

day of Christmas my true love gave to me

Two tawny tabbies,

and a kitten in a fir tree.

On the **third**

day of Christmas my true love gave to me

Three friendly felines,
two tawny tabbies,
and a kitten in a fir tree.

On the fourth
day of Christmas my true love gave to me

Four calico cats,

three friendly felines,

two tawny tabbies,

and a kitten in a fir tree.

On the fifth

day of Christmas my true love gave to me

Five golden kings,

four calico cats,

three friendly felines,

two tawny tabbies,

and a kitten in a fir tree.

On the sixth

day of Christmas my true love gave to me

Six Persians playing,

five golden kings,

four calico cats,

three friendly felines,

two tawny tabbies,

and a kitten in a fir tree.

On the seventh

day of Christmas my true love gave to me

Seven Siamese singing,

six Persians playing,

five golden kings,

four calico cats,

three friendly felines,

two tawny tabbies,

and a kitten in a fir tree.

On the eighth

day of Christmas my true love gave to me

Eight marvelous Manxes,

seven Siamese singing,

six Persians playing,

five golden kings,

four calico cats,

three friendly felines,

two tawny tabbies,

and a kitten in a fir tree.

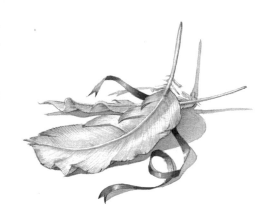

On the ninth

day of Christmas my true love gave to me

Nine lovely lynxes,
eight marvelous Manxes,
seven Siamese singing,
six Persians playing,
five golden kings,

four calico cats,
three friendly felines,
two tawny tabbies,
and a kitten in a fir tree.

On the tenth

day of Christmas my true love gave to me

Ten leopards lounging,   five golden kings,
nine lovely lynxes,   four calico cats,
eight marvelous Manxes,   three friendly felines,
seven Siamese singing,   two tawny tabbies,
six Persians playing,   and a kitten in a fir tree.

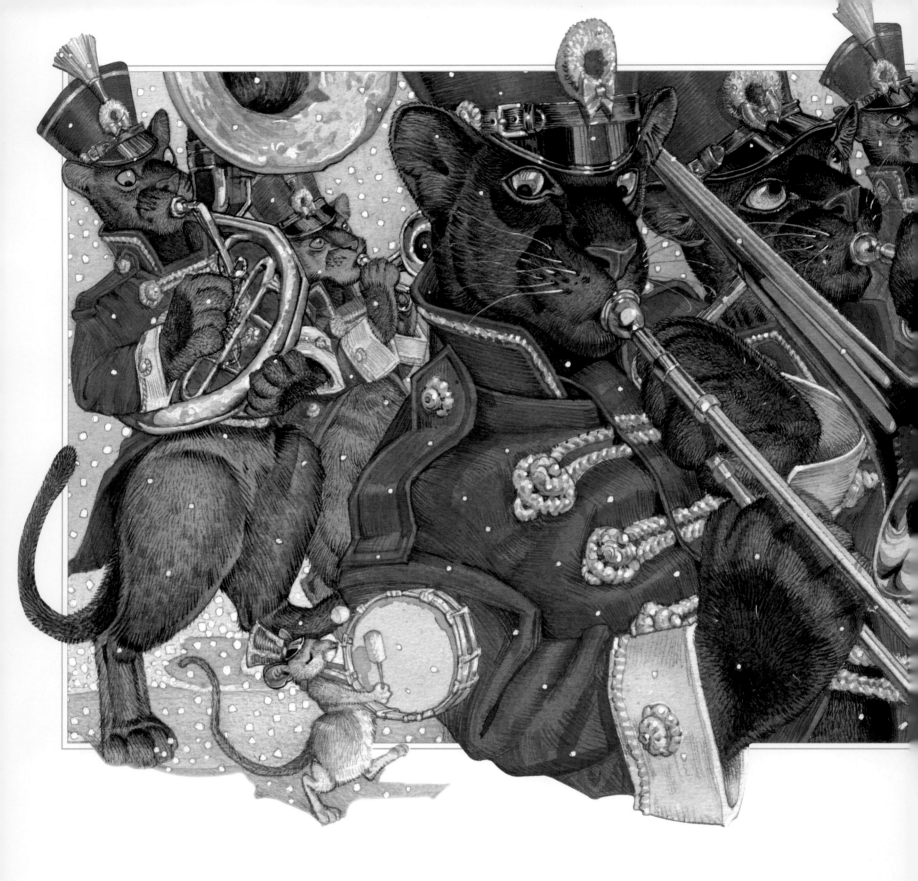

On the eleventh

day of Christmas my true love gave to me

Eleven panthers prancing,
ten leopards lounging,
nine lovely lynxes,
eight marvelous Manxes,
seven Siamese singing,
six Persians playing,
five golden kings,
four calico cats,
three friendly felines,
two tawny tabbies,
and a kitten in a fir tree.

On the twelfth

day of Christmas my true love gave to me

Twelve dapper dancers,

eleven panthers prancing,

ten leopards lounging,

nine lovely lynxes,

eight marvelous Manxes,

seven Siamese singing,

six Persians playing,

five golden kings,

four calico cats,

three friendly felines,

two tawny tabbies,

and a kitten in a fir tree.

ON THE **first** DAY OF CHRISTMAS
MY TRUE LOVE GAVE TO ME
A kitten in a fir tree.

ON THE **second** DAY OF CHRISTMAS
MY TRUE LOVE GAVE TO ME
Two tawny tabbies
And a kitten in a fir tree.

ON THE **third** DAY OF CHRISTMAS
MY TRUE LOVE GAVE TO ME
Three friendly felines,
Two tawny tabbies,
And a kitten in a fir tree.

ON THE **fourth** DAY OF CHRISTMAS
MY TRUE LOVE GAVE TO ME
Four calico cats,
Three friendly felines,
Two tawny tabbies,
And a kitten in a fir tree.

ON THE **fifth** DAY OF CHRISTMAS
MY TRUE LOVE GAVE TO ME
Five golden kings,
Four calico cats,
Three friendly felines,
Two tawny tabbies,
And a kitten in a fir tree.

ON THE **sixth** DAY OF CHRISTMAS
MY TRUE LOVE GAVE TO ME
Six Persians playing,
Five golden kings,
Four calico cats,
Three friendly felines,
Two tawny tabbies,
And a kitten in a fir tree.

ON THE **seventh** DAY OF CHRISTMAS
MY TRUE LOVE GAVE TO ME
Seven Siamese singing,
Six Persians playing,
Five golden kings,
Four calico cats,
Three friendly felines,
Two tawny tabbies,
And a kitten in a fir tree.

ON THE **eighth** DAY OF CHRISTMAS
MY TRUE LOVE GAVE TO ME
Eight marvelous Manxes,
Seven Siamese singing,
Six Persians playing,
Five golden kings,
Four calico cats,
Three friendly felines,
Two tawny tabbies,
And a kitten in a fir tree.

ON THE **ninth** DAY OF CHRISTMAS
MY TRUE LOVE GAVE TO ME
Nine lovely lynxes,
Eight marvelous Manxes,
Seven Siamese singing,
Six Persians playing,
Five golden kings,
Four calico cats,
Three friendly felines,
Two tawny tabbies,
And a kitten in a fir tree.

ON THE **tenth** DAY OF CHRISTMAS
MY TRUE LOVE GAVE TO ME
Ten leopards lounging,
Nine lovely lynxes,
Eight marvelous Manxes,
Seven Siamese singing,
Six Persians playing,
Five golden kings,
Four calico cats,
Three friendly felines,
Two tawny tabbies,
And a kitten in a fir tree.

ON THE **eleventh** DAY OF CHRISTMAS
MY TRUE LOVE GAVE TO ME
Eleven panthers prancing,
Ten leopards lounging,

Nine lovely lynxes,
Eight marvelous Manxes,
Seven Siamese singing,
Six Persians playing,
Five golden kings,
Four calico cats,
Three friendly felines,
Two tawny tabbies,
And a kitten in a fir tree.

ON THE **twelfth** DAY OF CHRISTMAS
MY TRUE LOVE GAVE TO ME
Twelve dapper dancers,
Eleven panthers prancing,
Ten leopards lounging,
Nine lovely lynxes,
Eight marvelous Manxes,
Seven Siamese singing,
Six Persians playing,
Five golden kings,
Four calico cats,
Three friendly
felines,
Two tawny tabbies,
And a kitten in
a fir tree.

The End